Grade **1**

Scott Foresman

Fresh Reads
for Differentiated Test Practice

D1157521

PEARSON

Scott Foresman

Editorial Offices: Glenview, Illinois • Parsippany, New Jersey • New York, New York
Sales Offices: Needham, Massachusetts • Duluth, Georgia • Glenview, Illinois
Coppell, Texas • Sacramento, California • Mesa, Arizona

ISBN: 0-328-16977-3

3 4 5 6 7 8 9 10 V004 14 13 12 11 10 09 08 07 06 05

Contents

Unit 1 Animals, Tame and Wild

Unit 2 Communities

Unit 3 Changes

Unit 4 Treasures

Unit 5 Great Ideas

Look at the pictures. Answer the questions that follow.

Jason Learns to Ride

Turn

Answer the questions below.

1 **What did Jason do** *first?*

○ He rode his bike.

○ He put on his helmet.

○ He got help from Mom.

2 **How did Jason feel** *before* **he rode his bike?**

○ happy

○ sleepy

○ scared

3 **How did Jason feel** *after* **he rode his bike?**

○ happy

○ sad

○ angry

4 **How does Jason feel about riding a bike?**

_____

- -

_____

_____

- -

_____

_____

- -

_____

_____

- -

_____

_____

- -

_____

Name _____

Look at the pictures. Answer the questions that follow.

The Playful Girl

Turn the page

- -

Fresh Reads   Unit 1 Week 1 OL

Answer the questions below.

1 **What did the girl do *first?***

  ○ She watched the rain.

  ○ She played ball.

  ○ She rode her bike.

2 **What does the girl like to do?**

  ○ She likes to play.

  ○ She likes to sit.

  ○ She likes to read.

3 **How does the girl feel when she plays?**

  ○ sad

  ○ happy

  ○ tired

4 **How does the girl feel when it rains?**

  ○ happy

  ○ sleepy

  ○ sad

5 **What does the girl like doing outside?**

_____

_____

_____

_____

_____

Read the selection. Answer the questions that follow.

Dan's Cat

Dan has a little cat. The cat is Rags. Dad is mad at Rags.

Rags gets in Dad's bag. Dad can see Dan and Rags play. Dan

and Rags play in the green grass. Then, Rags naps on Dan's

lap. Dan pats Rags on the back. Rags is happy. Dan is glad to

have Rags as a pal.

Answer the questions below.

1 **Why is Dad mad?**

- ○ Rags hurt Dad.
- ○ Rags gets in Dad's bag.
- ○ Rags is lost.

2 **How does Dan feel about Rags?**

- ○ mad
- ○ sad
- ○ glad

3 **What do Rags and Dan do just after they play?**

- ○ Rags takes a nap.
- ○ Dad gets mad.
- ○ Dan pats Rags.

4 **What does Dan do for Rags?**

_____

- -

_____

_____

- -

_____

- -

_____

5 **How does Rags feel about Dan?**

_____

- -

_____

© Pearson Education 1

Name _____

Look at the pictures. Answer the questions that follow.

The Lion and the Monkey

Turn the page

Answer the questions below.

1 **What can not really happen?**

○ Trees grow in a forest.

○ Animals live in a forest.

○ Animals eat at a table.

2 **The monkey was**

○ kind to the lion.

○ mean to the lion.

○ afraid of the lion.

3 **A real lion does not**

○ eat.

○ wear clothes.

○ have fur.

4 **What could really happen in this story?**

_____

- -

_____

- -

_____

_____

- -

_____

- -

_____

- -

_____

Name _____

Look at the picture. Answer the questions that follow.

Fun at the Beach

Turn the page.

Answer the questions below.

1 **How does the mouse feel?**

    ○ happy

    ○ sad

    ○ hungry

2 **How can you tell this is make-believe?**

    ○ There is sand at the beach.

    ○ There are waves in the water.

    ○ A mouse uses a shovel.

3 **What can really happen?**

    ○ A pig reads.

    ○ A dog sleeps.

    ○ A fox uses a fork.

4 **A real fox does not**

    ○ eat.

    ○ have ears.

    ○ sit in a beach chair.

5 **What can not really happen?**

_____

- -

_____

- -

_____

_____

- -

_____

Read the selection. Answer the questions that follow.

Max on a Trip

Dear Jack,

I was on a trip with my cat, Sam. I had my hat and a pack on my back. Sam had his cap. We saw Tim. Tim was a big green cat.

Tim said, "Come and play tag with me!"

We did. We had a snack and a nap. Then Sam and I ran back.

From,

Max

Answer the questions below.

1 **What can not really happen?**

- ○ Max has a snack.
- ○ Max has a nap.
- ○ A cat talks to Max.

2 **Max is**

- ○ silly.
- ○ mean.
- ○ bad.

3 **What can really happen?**

- ○ A cat can talk.
- ○ A boy can have a hat.
- ○ A cat can have a cap.

4 **What is something that Max really did?**

_____

_____

_____

_____

_____

5 **How do you know this story is make-believe?**

_____

_____

_____

_____

_____

Look at the pictures. Answer the questions that follow.

Ling Plays Ball

Turn the page.

Answer the questions below.

1. **Ling likes to**

○ play t-ball.

○ take walks.

○ cook.

2 **Where does this story take place?**

○ at Ling's home

○ at a park

○ at a store

3 **How did Ling feel when she hit the ball?**

○ sad

○ angry

○ happy

4 **How can you tell this story could really happen?**

_____

- -

_____

_____

- -

_____

_____

- -

_____

_____

- -

_____

Look at the picture. Answer the questions that follow.

On a Trip

Turn the page.

Answer the questions below.

1 **The boy and the dog are**

- ○ friendly.
- ○ mean.
- ○ mad.

2 **How can you tell this story is make-believe?**

- ○ The boy has a pet dog.
- ○ The boy and the dog are in space.
- ○ There are stars.

3 **How does the boy feel?**

- ○ happy
- ○ angry
- ○ scared

4 **Where does this story happen?**

- ○ in a park
- ○ at a school
- ○ in space

5 **How does Zam feel when he sees the boy and dog?**

_____

_____

_____

_____

Read the selection. Answer the questions that follow.

Fox's Box

Fox got in the big box at the pond. The box left the dock. It did not stop. Fox was not glad. He did not like to get wet. He had to get back to land.

"Help!" Fox said.

"Hop in the pond!" said Fish. "You can do it! Come with me!"

Fox did it, and he got back to land.

Turn the page.

Answer the questions below.

1 **Where was Fox?**

- ○ on a hill
- ○ at a pond
- ○ at his house

2 **How did Fox feel when the box went in the pond?**

- ○ funny
- ○ happy
- ○ scared

3 **Fish likes to**

- ○ help.
- ○ run.
- ○ sit.

4 **How did Fox feel at the end of the story?**

_____

- -

_____

_____

- -

_____

5 **How do you know this story is make-believe?**

_____

- -

_____

_____

- -

_____

Name _____

Look at the pictures. Answer the questions that follow.

The Family

1.

2.

3.

4.

Turn the page.

- -

Answer the questions below.

1 **What is the story mostly about?**

   ○ a new baby

   ○ food

   ○ grandparents

2 **What would be another good title for this story?**

   ○ A Big House

   ○ Baby Comes Home

   ○ Time for Bed

3 **What is the big idea of the *last* picture?**

   ○ playing with the baby

   ○ playing with toys

   ○ playing outside

4 **Why do you think the family looks tired at breakfast?**

_____

- -

_____

- -

_____

- -

_____

_____

- -

_____

- -

Look at the pictures. Answer the questions that follow.

The Builders

Answer the questions below.

1 **Who do these pictures tell about?**

○ a girl

○ a family

○ a girl and a boy

2 **What is this story mostly about?**

○ A boy and a girl build with blocks.

○ A girl helps.

○ A boy makes something.

3 **The boy and girl**

○ work together.

○ play ball.

○ read to each other.

4 **What is another good title for this story?**

○ A Block

○ A Tall Building

○ A Little Boy

5 **How do you think the girl and boy feel at the end of the story?**

_____

- -

_____

_____

- -

_____

_____

- -

_____

Read the selection. Answer the questions that follow.

Bob's Job

Bob has to get dinner for his animals. He is glad to do it. He takes seeds to them.

"Eat this up! It will help you get big!"

The animals like to eat. Lots of little birds come to get a snack. Bob likes to watch. He sees five yellow birds. He sees two blue birds. Bob likes doing his job.

© Pearson Education 1

Turn the page.

Answer the questions below.

1 **What is this story all about?**

○ playing in the yard

○ getting big and strong

○ feeding animals and watching birds

2 **What is another good title for this story?**

○ Yellow Birds

○ Bob and the Animals

○ Birds Fly Away

3 **Why did lots of little birds come?**

○ They were hungry.

○ They wanted to play.

○ They were hot.

4 **Why did Bob have seeds?**

_____

_____

_____

_____

5 **What happened at the end of the story?**

_____

_____

_____

_____

Look at the pictures. Answer the questions that follow.

Camping

Turn the page.

Answer the questions below.

1 **What can not be real?**

- ○ Stars are in the sky.
- ○ A cat drives.
- ○ Dad makes a fire.

2 **How can you tell this story is make-believe?**

- ○ The animals are not like real animals.
- ○ The story is about a family.
- ○ The dog has a tail.

3 **The last picture happens**

- ○ at noon.
- ○ in the morning.
- ○ at night.

4 **What in this story could happen?**

_____

_____

_____

_____

_____

_____

_____

_____

_____

Look at the picture. Answer the questions that follow.

Jack and the Beanstalk

Turn the page.

Answer the questions below.

1 **What can really happen?**

○ A boy can climb to the sky.

○ A goose can lay an egg.

○ A man can live in the sky.

2 **How do you know this story is make-believe?**

○ There is a giant.

○ There is a goose.

○ There is a boy.

3 **What can not happen?**

○ A man can have a goose.

○ A boy can climb.

○ A man can walk on clouds.

4 **What can not be real?**

○ a cloud

○ a castle in the sky

○ an egg

5 **What tells you that the story happens in the sky?**

_____

- -

_____

_____

- -

_____

_____

- -

_____

Read the selection. Answer the questions that follow.

Kim's Dinner

Kim and her pals eat dinner in the grass. Kim and her pals see a cat, a pig, and a fox.

Kim said, "Can you sing a song, Cat?"

"Yes!" said Cat. And he did.

"Can you hop on one leg, Pig?" said Kim.

"Yes!" said Pig. And he did.

"Can you do tricks, Fox?" Kim said.

"Yes!" said Fox. And he did.

They had fun.

Turn the page.

Answer the questions below.

1 **What can not really happen?**

○ A cat can sing a song.

○ A girl can eat dinner.

○ Pals can have fun.

2 **Where did Kit have dinner?**

○ on the grass

○ at school

○ in the park

3 **What can really happen?**

○ A cat can sing.

○ A girl eats.

○ A pig talks.

4 **How do you know the fox is not real?**

_____

- -

_____

5 **What is something in the story that can really happen?**

_____

- -

_____

_____

- -

_____

_____

- -

_____

Look at the pictures. Answer the questions that follow.

Dad and Anna Go Shopping

Turn the page.

Answer the questions below.

1 **How are bananas, apples, and grapes the same?**

- ○ They all are yellow.
- ○ They all are fruit.
- ○ They all are long.

2 **Why did Dad and Anna go shopping?**

- ○ They needed food.
- ○ They had dropped their eggs.
- ○ They were bored.

3 **Why did Dad and Anna clean the floor?**

- ○ They went shopping.
- ○ Dad spilled milk.
- ○ Anna dropped an egg.

4 **Why did Anna drop an egg?**

Look at the pictures. Answer the questions that follow.

In the Garden

Turn the page.

Answer the questions below.

1 **What does not belong on a plant?**

- ○ a leaf
- ○ a flower
- ○ a shovel

2 **Why did the girl and her mom dig a hole?**

- ○ They were planting a bush.
- ○ They were making mud pies.
- ○ They were hiding a box.

3 **Why did the girl water the plant?**

- ○ to make it go away
- ○ to help it grow
- ○ to clean it

4 **Why did the girl and her mom wear gloves?**

- ○ to keep their hands safe
- ○ to stay warm
- ○ to look nice

5 **Why is the girl happy at the end of the story?**

_____

- -

_____

_____

- -

_____

_____

- -

_____

Read the selection. Answer the questions that follow.

Ron

Ron is sick. He will not go to class. He is at home with Dad. He will not take a nap. He can read an animal book for fun. It has a hippo, an elephant, and a zebra. Now Ron is playing with his cat. But Ron must rest. Then Ron will not be sick.

Turn the page.

Answer the questions below.

1 **Why didn't Ron go to class?**

   ○ It is raining.

   ○ He is sick.

   ○ It is summer.

2 **Why did Ron read a book?**

   ○ to learn about the zoo

   ○ He had homework.

   ○ He was not tired.

3 **How are a hippo, an elephant, and a zebra the same?**

   ○ They are zoo animals.

   ○ They live in the water.

   ○ They are all toys.

4 **Why must Ron rest?**

_____

_____

_____

5 **Why did Ron feel better?**

_____

_____

_____

Look at the pictures. Answer the questions that follow.

Mr. Cat and Miss Bunny

Turn the page.

Answer the questions below.

1 How can you tell this story is make-believe?

○ The animals act like humans.

○ The cat has a long tail.

○ The rabbit has long ears.

2 What is this story all about?

○ friends getting together

○ going out for a walk

○ drinking milk

3 What is another good title for this story?

○ Bunny Waits for Cat

○ Animal Houses

○ Bunny's Visit with Cat

4 What is the last picture mostly about?

_____

- -

_____

_____

- -

_____

_____

- -

_____

_____

- -

_____

_____

- -

Read the selection. Answer the questions that follow.

Fun Walks

Fox likes to take a walk. She walks to town. Then she

walks to the park. On her walk, she sees bugs. She sees ducks.

She sees the sun. Then Fox walks home. At home she talks to

her dad. She tells him what she saw. She tells him of the fun

she had on her walk.

Turn the page.

Answer the questions below.

1 **What is the story all about?**
- ○ Fox plays with ducks.
- ○ Fox likes to walk.
- ○ Fox talks to her dad.

2 **This story is mostly about**
- ○ Fox.
- ○ Dad.
- ○ bugs.

3 **What best tells what Fox sees on her walks?**
- ○ She sees many things.
- ○ She sees her dad.
- ○ She sees birds at the park.

4 **At home, Fox talks mostly about**
- ○ the bugs.
- ○ the sun.
- ○ the things she saw.

5 **How do you know this story is make-believe?**

_____

- -

_____

_____

- -

_____

_____

- -

_____

Read the selection. Answer the questions that follow.

Look, Look, Look

Fred said, "I want to play ball. Sam and Pam, do you want to play ball with me?"

"Yes!" said Sam and Pam.

Fred asked, "Do you have a ball?"

They did not have a ball. They all went looking for a ball.

They went looking at home. They went looking in the park.

Then Fred saw his dog Zip. Zip had a ball with him! Then

Fred, Sam, Pam, and Zip had fun playing ball in the park.

Turn the page.

Answer the questions below.

1 **What did Fred want to do?**
○ walk
○ play
○ sit

2 **What is another good name for this story?**
○ The Park
○ Pam and Sam
○ Zip's Ball

3 **What happens at the end of the story?**
○ Fred finds a ball.
○ Fred looks for a ball.
○ Fred runs home.

4 **What is this story all about?**

_____

- -

_____

- -

_____

5 **How can you tell that this story could really happen?**

_____

- -

_____

- -

_____

Look at the picture. Answer the questions that follow.

Jane's Juice

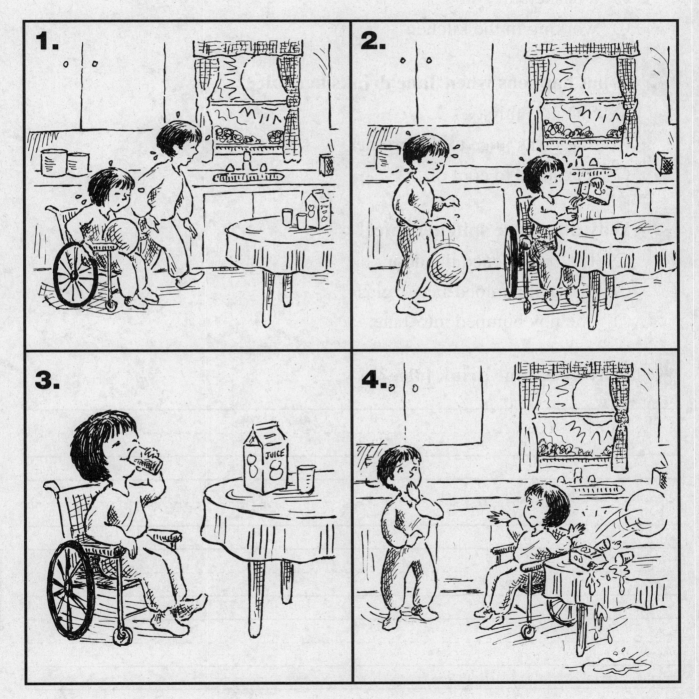

Turn the page.

Answer the questions below.

1 **What is the story all about?**

○ drinking and spilling juice

○ a basketball game

○ working in the kitchen

2 **What happens when Jane drinks her juice?**

○ She gets thirsty.

○ She gives juice to her brother.

○ She starts to cool off.

3 **Why does Jane spill her juice?**

○ The boy opened the door.

○ The ball bumped Jane's glass.

○ The boy bumped into Jane.

4 **Why does Jane drink juice?**

_____

- -

_____

- -

_____

- -

_____

- -

_____

- -

_____

- -

_____

Read the selection. Answer the questions that follow.

What Mom Makes

Sam is six! Mom wants to make a little cake for him. She must mix it up. Then she bakes the cake. It is yellow. Sam likes yellow. Sam's pals come to his home. Mom gets the cake for them. They sit and eat it. It is good! Mom could have made a big cake!

Turn the page.

Answer the questions below.

1 **What is the story all about?**

○ a home for Sam and Mom

○ the color yellow

○ a cake for Sam and his pals

2 **Why did Mom make the cake?**

○ Sam was six.

○ It was her big day.

○ She wanted to eat cake.

3 **Why did Sam's pals come to his home?**

○ to eat cake

○ to see Mom

○ to bake a cake

4 **Why did Mom make a yellow cake?**

○ Mom likes yellow.

○ Sam likes yellow.

○ Sam's pals like yellow.

5 **Why could Mom have made a big cake?**

_____

_____

_____

_____

_____

_____

Read the selection. Answer the questions that follow.

Nate Gets to Play

Nate plays in the park. He runs and he jumps. He plays in the sand. He makes animals with the sand. Then the rain falls, and Nate must go home. At home Nate puts on dry socks. Then he takes a nap. Nate wakes up and sees that the sun is back. Nate smiles. He gets up and walks back to the park. He is glad that the sun shines.

Turn the page.

Answer the questions below.

1 **Why did Nate go to the park?**

- ○ to have fun
- ○ to see the rain
- ○ to take a nap

2 **Why did Nate go home?**

- ○ It was too hot.
- ○ He was sick.
- ○ The rain fell.

3 **What is another good name for this story?**

- ○ Nate Takes a Nap
- ○ Rain and Sun
- ○ The Sun

4 **Why did Nate put on dry socks?**

_____

- -

_____

_____

- -

_____

5 **Why did Nate smile at the end of the story?**

_____

- -

_____

_____

- -

_____

Look at the picture. Answer the questions that follow.

Bike Safety

This is NOT safe.

This is safe.

Turn the page.

Answer the questions below.

1 **The author wants you to**
- ○ know about the girl's family.
- ○ learn how to ride a bike.
- ○ stay safe while riding a bike.

2 **Why did the author write this?**
- ○ to make you laugh
- ○ to teach you something
- ○ to tell a make-believe story

3 **Which sentence tells about the pictures?**
- ○ The girl needs to be careful.
- ○ The girl likes to run.
- ○ The bike is new.

4 **Why do you think the author uses two pictures of the girl?**

_____

_____

_____

_____

_____

_____

_____

_____

Read the selection. Answer the questions that follow.

We See Animals

We can see animals in many places. I have a cat at home. A red bird has a nest in my back tree. Animals live at the animal park too. We see the little whales that live there. We see hippos in the pond. At home or at the animal park, we can see many animals.

Turn the page.

Answer the questions below.

1 **The author wants you to**

   ○ look at birds.

   ○ see the trees.

   ○ see that animals live in many places.

2 **Why did the author write about his cat?**

   ○ It is one animal he sees.

   ○ It is fun.

   ○ He does not have a dog.

3 **This story is**

   ○ sad.

   ○ real.

   ○ funny.

4 **The author does not try to**

   ○ tell about hippos.

   ○ talk about the animal park.

   ○ make you sad.

5 **What is this story mostly about?**

_____

- -

_____

_____

- -

_____

_____

- -

_____

Read the selection. Answer the questions that follow.

Why I Like My Neighborhood

I am a big cat. I am glad I live on Pine Drive. My

neighborhood has nice people. The man in the yellow house

feeds me. The mail people stop to pet me. Miss MacDonald

puts out milk for me. The milk is good. The mice are not

too busy to chase me. The birds sing to me all the time. My

neighborhood is the best place!

Turn the page.

Answer the questions below.

1 **Why did the author write this story?**
- ○ to make you smile
- ○ to make you cry
- ○ to tell you about a man

2 **This story is**
- ○ scary.
- ○ happy.
- ○ sad.

3 **Why did the author write about milk?**
- ○ The author likes milk.
- ○ The cat likes milk.
- ○ There is no water.

4 **What is this story mostly about?**

_____

- - - - - - - - - - - - - - - - - - -

_____

- - - - - - - - - - - - - - - - - - -

_____

5 **What is funny about mice running after a cat?**

_____

- - - - - - - - - - - - - - - - - - -

_____

_____

- - - - - - - - - - - - - - - - - - -

_____

Look at the pictures. Answer the questions that follow.

Jack Needs a Snack

Turn the page.

Answer the questions below.

1 **Why did Jack make a sandwich?**

◯ His dad told him to make one.

◯ He was hungry.

◯ He wanted to feed the cat.

2 **What happened first in the story?**

◯ Jack poured some milk.

◯ Jack ate a sandwich.

◯ Jack read a book.

3 **What happened next in the story?**

◯ Jack made a sandwich.

◯ Jack left the kitchen.

◯ Jack drank some milk.

4 **What was the last thing that happened in the story?**

_____

- -

_____

- -

_____

- -

_____

- -

_____

Read the selection. Answer the questions that follow.

Nice People

Kim came into my class late in the fall. No one said much to her. Then at lunch Jan sat with Kim. Kim was glad. Jan gave grapes to Kim. Kim gave cake to Jan. Then they were pals.

When Jeff came to class, Kim was nice to him. She said, "We can all sit together at lunch."

Turn the page.

Answer the questions below.

1 **Why did Jan give grapes to Kim?**

○ She wanted to be nice to Kim.

○ She had too many grapes.

○ She wanted to eat cake.

2 **What happened first?**

○ Jeff came to class.

○ Jan talked to Kim.

○ Kim came to class.

3 **What happened after the girls had lunch?**

○ Kim sat down with Jan.

○ They became good friends.

○ Jan went to a new school.

4 **What happened last?**

○ Kim sat with Jan.

○ Kim talked to Jeff.

○ Jeff came to class.

5 **What happened after Jan gave Kim grapes?**

_____

_____

_____

_____

_____

© Pearson Education 1

Read the selection. Answer the questions that follow.

My Cake for Bill

My name is Jill. My twin is Bill. We are now six! I want to make a cake for Bill. I mix it up. I put it into a pan. Then Mom and I bake the cake. We put yellow frosting on it. I put six candles on the cake. Mom lit the candles. We sing to Bill. He claps his hands. Then he puffs and puffs but he can not make the candles go out. They are trick candles. What fun!

Turn the page.

Answer the questions below.

1 **The first thing Jill did to the cake was**

   ○ bake it.

   ○ mix it.

   ○ put it in a pan.

2 **After Jill puts frosting on the cake, she**

   ○ puts candles on it.

   ○ claps her hands.

   ○ helps Bill.

3 **What did Bill do last?**

   ○ clap

   ○ bake

   ○ blow

4 **Why do Mom and Jill sing to Bill?**

_____

_____

_____

5 **What could Bill do next?**

_____

_____

_____

_____

_____

_____

Look at the picture. Answer the questions that follow.

The Silly Race

Turn the page.

Answer the questions below.

1 **Who wrote the book?**

○ Cat

○ Jan Todd

○ Mouse

2 **Why do you think the author wrote *The Silly Race?***

○ to teach you about races

○ to make you sad

○ to make you laugh

3 **Why are there make-believe animals in the book?**

○ to be funny

○ to be scary

○ to show how animals live

4 **Why is Mouse smiling?**

_____

- -

_____

- -

_____

- -

_____

- -

_____

- -

_____

Read the selection. Answer the questions that follow.

My Brave Mom

My mom has a good job. Her job is to put out fires. She

puts on a big black hat with a wide brim for her job. She

drives a red truck. She helps people in the neighborhood. She

is brave. I am glad when she comes home safe. When I grow

up, I want to put out fires too.

Turn the page.

Answer the questions below.

1 **Why do you think the author wants to put out fires?**

- ○ He wants to be like his mom.
- ○ He likes hats.
- ○ He likes trucks.

2 **Why did the author write this story?**

- ○ to tell about a red truck
- ○ to tell about his mom
- ○ to tell about his neighborhood

3 **This story is**

- ○ real.
- ○ fun.
- ○ sad.

4 **Why did the author tell about Mom's hat?**

- ○ to tell when she works
- ○ to tell where she lives
- ○ to tell what she looks like

5 **Why does the author think his mom is brave?**

_____

_____

_____

_____

_____

_____

Read the selection. Answer the questions that follow.

A New Pal

Dear Kip,

    I have a new pal. He just came to this neighborhood. He

lives down the block from me. His name is Jack. He is fun.

He is nice too. Jack likes to play ball. He can hit the ball far.

He likes to run races. He can run fast. We play together all the

time. We have a good time. I am glad I met him.

               Still your good pal,

               Rick

© Pearson Education 1

Turn the page.

Answer the questions below.

1 **Why is the name of this story "A New Pal"?**

○ It is about Jack.

○ It is about a race.

○ It is about a ball.

2 **This letter is**

○ sad.

○ real.

○ silly.

3 **Which of these tells how Rick feels about Jack?**

○ His name is Jack.

○ He can run fast.

○ I am glad I met him.

4 **Why does Rick like Jack?**

_____

_____

_____

_____

5 **How can you tell Rick and Kip are pals?**

_____

_____

_____

_____

Look at the pictures. Answer the questions that follow.

Seasons

Turn the page.

Answer the questions below.

1 **What is the same in each picture?**

- ○ the lamps
- ○ the weather outside
- ○ the snow

2 **The author wants you to**

- ○ learn how birds fly.
- ○ feel sad.
- ○ see how the weather changes.

3 **Which things are in all three pictures?**

- ○ the boy, the bed, the lamps
- ○ the bed, the snow, the curtains
- ○ the boy, the rain, the lamps

4 **What is different in all the pictures?**

_____

- -

_____

_____

- -

_____

_____

- -

_____

_____

- -

_____

Read the selection. Answer the questions that follow.

A Family

A family can be big or small. Dan has a family with a mom, dad, and nine children. Ann lives with just her mom. Tom lives with his dad. Ben lives with his mom and his dad. Max has a family that lives together in a big neighborhood. Pete's family lives in many places. A family can come in many shapes and sizes!

Turn the page.

Answer the questions below.

1 **Who has a big family?**

○ Ann

○ Dan

○ Tom

2 **Who has a small family?**

○ Ann

○ Dan

○ Pete

3 **Why does the author say that a family can be big or small?**

○ to show how families are the same

○ to show how families are different

○ to show different kinds of houses

4 **How is Max's family not like Pete's family?**

○ Max's family works hard.

○ Max's family has a son.

○ Max's family lives together.

5 **How are Ann's family and Tom's family the same?**

_____

- -

_____

_____

- -

_____

_____

- -

_____

Read the selection. Answer the questions that follow.

Two Rabbits

Two rabbits left the pet shop to live with a new family. Honey was a tan rabbit. She could live inside. Flower was a white rabbit. He got to live outside in a cage. Honey wanted to eat carrots and hay. Flower wanted to eat hay and rabbit food. Honey and Flower liked to hop around their new homes. Honey and Flower had little noses. They were nice rabbits.

Turn the page.

Answer the questions below.

1 **The author wrote this story to tell you about**

○ a new family.

○ all animals.

○ two rabbits.

2 **How are Honey and Flower the same?**

○ They are tan.

○ They live with a family.

○ They are white.

3 **How is Honey not like Flower?**

○ Honey lives inside.

○ Honey is big.

○ Honey likes to hop.

4 **What do both rabbits like to eat?**

_____

_____

_____

_____

5 **How do the rabbits look different?**

_____

_____

_____

_____

© Pearson Education 1

Read the selection. Answer the questions that follow.

Jen Is Six

Jen is now six. Her pals come to see her. Kim has a big

blue box for Jen. Mike has a small red one. Jen has good cake

for them to eat.

Turn the page.

Answer the questions below.

1 **How are Jen, Kim, and Mike the same?**

  ◯ They all eat cake.

  ◯ They all get a box.

  ◯ They all are six.

2 **Who came with a red box?**

  ◯ Kim

  ◯ Jen

  ◯ Mike

3 **How are Mike and Kim the same?**

  ◯ They have a gift for Jen.

  ◯ They do not like cake.

  ◯ They have bikes.

4 **Why do you think the author wrote this story?**

_____

_____

_____

_____

_____

_____

_____

_____

_____

Read the selection. Answer the questions that follow.

Wind and Ice

Some days are so cold! Cold winds come. There is ice.

Bears go to caves to sleep. Children have mittens and hats so

they can play outside. Small children like to run in the cold.

Big children like to skate on the ice. They all ride on sleds.

They slide down the white hills. Cold days are fun!

Turn the page.

Answer the questions below.

1 **How are bears not like the children?**

   ○ Bears have mittens and hats.

   ○ Bears like to run in the cold.

   ○ Bears sleep when it is cold.

2 **The author wrote this story to**

   ○ tell you real things.

   ○ make you feel sad.

   ○ teach you how to skate.

3 **How are small children and big children the same?**

   ○ They all go out to play.

   ○ They all skate on the ice.

   ○ They all run in the cold.

4 **How are big children not like small children?**

   ○ Big children have mittens.

   ○ Big children like to skate.

   ○ Big children go to caves.

5 **How are mittens and hats alike?**

_____

_____

_____

_____

_____

_____

Read the selection. Answer the questions that follow.

A. J. and C. J.

A. J. and C. J. are twins, but they are different. A. J. is a boy, and he is big. He likes lunch the best. He plays in the day and sleeps at night. C. J. is a girl, and she is small. She likes dinner the best. She plays at night and sleeps in the day. They both live in the zoo. A. J. and C. J. are bears!

Turn the page.

Answer the questions below.

1 **How are A. J. and C. J. the same?**

○ They sleep at night.

○ They are the same age.

○ They are the same size.

2 **How are A. J. and C. J. different?**

○ A. J. is a boy, and C. J. is a girl.

○ A. J. walks, and C. J. runs.

○ A. J. is black, and C. J. is brown.

3 **Who likes lunch the best?**

○ C. J.

○ C. J. and A. J.

○ A. J.

4 **How do you know that A. J. and C. J. are real bears?**

_____

_____

_____

_____

5 **Why does the author wait until the end to tell you that A. J. and C. J. are bears?**

_____

_____

_____

_____

Read the selection. Answer the questions that follow.

Dog and the Odd Stone

When Dog finds a stone in the forest, he is not the same.

He can now talk! But Dog does not like talking. So he takes

the stone back to the forest.

Turn the page.

Answer the questions below.

1 **How does the story begin?**

○ Dog is at home.

○ Dog can talk.

○ Dog finds a stone.

2 **What happens in the middle of the story?**

○ Dog can talk.

○ Dog finds a stone.

○ Dog likes to talk.

3 **How does the story end?**

○ Dog takes the stone back.

○ Dog can talk.

○ Dog finds a stone.

4 **Do you think Dog can talk before he finds the stone? Why or why not?**

_____

_____

_____

_____

_____

_____

_____

Read the selection. Answer the questions that follow.

The Hummingbird

There was a bird who could not sing. He could just hum. Other birds sang sweet tunes. But this bird wanted to sing nice songs of his own. He made a wish. Then a girl walked by his tree. She sang to him. He so wanted to sing back to her. And then he could! He sang beautiful songs to her!

Turn the page.

Answer the questions below.

1 **Before the bird made a wish**

○ a girl walked by his tree.

○ he could just hum.

○ he did not want to sing.

2 **How did the story begin?**

○ The bird was happy.

○ The bird made a nest.

○ The bird could not sing.

3 **What happened in the middle of the story?**

○ A girl sang to the bird.

○ The bird made a nest.

○ A girl made a wish.

4 **What did the bird do at the end of the story?**

○ He sang to the girl.

○ He made a wish.

○ He had to fly home.

5 **Why did the bird make a wish?**

_____

- -

_____

- -

_____

- -

_____

Read the selection. Answer the questions that follow.

Flower Garden

Rose wants a summer garden. She needs to plant some flower seeds. She has lots of work to do. First, Rose rakes the dirt. Next, she digs some holes. Then, she puts the seeds in the holes and puts dirt on top of the seeds. Last, Rose waters them with a hose. The seeds will grow soon. They will become beautiful flowers.

Turn the page.

Answer the questions below.

1 **What does Rose do at the beginning of the story?**

  ○ She waters the seeds.

  ○ She rakes the dirt.

  ○ She grows into a flower.

2 **In the middle of the story, Rose**

  ○ puts seeds in the holes.

  ○ wants a garden.

  ○ rakes up the dirt.

3 **What happens at the end of the story?**

  ○ Rose puts the flowers in a vase.

  ○ Rose digs holes in the dirt.

  ○ The seeds will begin to grow.

4 **What happens after the seeds are put in the holes?**

_____

- -

_____

- -

_____

5 **What will happen to the seeds last?**

_____

- -

_____

- -

_____

Read the selection. Answer the questions that follow.

Playing Together

Rose had a toy plane. Jim wanted to play with it.

Rose said, "No."

Jim said, "Share your plane with me. I will share my truck

with you."

Rose said, "Good!"

Turn the page.

Answer the questions below.

1 **What is the big idea in the story?**

○ Toy planes can be fun.

○ It is good to share.

○ Some kids like trucks.

2 **How did the story end?**

○ Rose was mad.

○ Rose did share the plane.

○ Jim came to play.

3 **How did Jim play with Rose?**

○ He shared his truck with her.

○ He took her plane away.

○ He made her go home.

4 **Give this story a new name.**

_____

- -

_____

_____

- -

_____

_____

- -

_____

_____

- -

_____

_____

- -

_____

Read the selection. Answer the questions that follow.

A Lesson for a Bee

Miss Bee was not a busy bee. Other bees flew from flower to flower. They got nectar. They made honey. They worked. Miss Bee just sat. Other bees asked her to help. She did not. Then the cold came. Miss Bee had nothing to eat. She looked for her friends. They gave her honey. She now sees that she needs to be busy.

Turn the page.

Answer the questions below.

1 What lesson did Miss Bee find out in this story?

○ Some bees need to rest.

○ Friends get nectar from flowers.

○ Every bee must keep busy.

2 Why didn't Miss Bee make honey?

○ She didn't like to work.

○ She was too busy.

○ She didn't like honey.

3 What happened to Miss Bee in the middle of the story?

○ She had no food to eat.

○ She helped her friends.

○ She flew from flower to flower.

4 What is the big idea of this story?

○ Honey is made from nectar.

○ You need to do your work.

○ Friends like to have flowers.

5 What lesson did you get from this story?

_____

- -

_____

_____

- -

_____

_____

- -

_____

Read the selection. Answer the questions that follow.

Bob's New School

I had to move to a house away from my friends. I did not want to go to a new school. Father said I could make new friends. He helped me feel better.

I took some toys I had made to my new school. The kids wanted to meet me and see my toys. They wanted to make some too. Soon we were friends!

Turn the page.

Answer the questions below.

1 **What is the big idea in this story?**
- ○ making toys
- ○ going to school
- ○ making new friends

2 **Why didn't Bob want to go to school?**
- ○ He was playing.
- ○ He didn't know the kids.
- ○ He was very tired.

3 **What would be another good name for this story?**
- ○ Making Friends
- ○ How to Make Your Own Toys
- ○ Bob's Old House

4 **What is this story all about?**

_____

_____

_____

5 **What happened to Bob at the end of the story?**

_____

_____

_____

Read the selection. Answer the questions that follow.

Ann Takes a Walk

"I will take you for a walk," Ann said to her dog. They went by the store. They ran in the park. Then they walked around the pond. They wanted to take naps when they got home.

Turn the page.

Answer the questions below.

1 **How does the story begin?**

○ Ann wants a nap.

○ Ann talks to her dog.

○ Ann walks around the pond.

2 **What happens in the middle of the story?**

○ Ann and her dog go for a walk.

○ Ann and her dog run to school.

○ Ann and her dog go back home.

3 **At the end of the story, Ann and her dog**

○ are home.

○ run in the park.

○ walk by the store.

4 **In what way are Ann and her dog the same after their walk?**

_____

- -

_____

_____

- -

_____

_____

- -

_____

_____

- -

_____

_____

Read the selection. Answer the questions that follow.

Rainy Day Fun

One day Rob and Tom woke up and looked out the window. They saw rain. The boys felt sad. They told Dad.

"What can we do now?" the boys asked Dad.

"We can ride our bikes together at the inside track on Main Street," Dad said with a smile.

Then Dad drove them to the track. They all rode their bikes and had fun inside. They were happy that it was a rainy day.

Turn the page.

Answer the questions below.

1 **How are Dad and the boys the same?**

   ○ They like to ride on bikes.

   ○ They get sad on rainy days.

   ○ They look out the window.

2 **What happens in this story?**

   ○ The boys and Dad ride bikes inside.

   ○ Dad gets the boys new bikes.

   ○ It rains for many days.

3 **How does this story begin?**

   ○ Rob and Tom feel happy.

   ○ Dad drives the boys to the inside track.

   ○ Rob and Tom see that it is raining.

4 **What happens in the middle of the story?**

   ○ Rob, Tom, and Dad ride their bikes.

   ○ Rob and Tom talk with Dad.

   ○ Rob and Tom feel sad.

5 **How does the story end?**

Read the selection. Answer the questions that follow.

Brave Frog

There was a frog that was afraid of rain. When it rained, he hid under leaves. One day it rained very hard. The frog heard shouting. A squirrel was in a net. The rain came down more. Soon the water would be over the squirrel's head. The frog came out from under the leaves. He ran in the rain. He wanted to save the squirrel. He did! The frog was not ever afraid of rain again.

Turn the page.

Answer the questions below.

1 **What was the frog afraid of at the beginning of the story?**

- ○ leaves
- ○ rain
- ○ a squirrel

2 **How was the frog the same as the squirrel?**

- ○ They both got wet.
- ○ They both liked the rain.
- ○ They both ran in the rain.

3 **Why did the squirrel shout?**

- ○ He wanted to play in the rain.
- ○ He needed a bath.
- ○ He was stuck in a net.

4 **What did the frog do at the beginning of the story?**

_____

_____

_____

5 **How did the frog change by the end of the story?**

_____

_____

_____

Read the selection. Answer the questions that follow.

The Twins

Jane and Mark are twins. Jane was born first. Then Mark was born. Jane likes to play ball and swim. Mark likes to brush his dog and pet his cat. Jane and Mark like reading.

Turn the page.

Answer the questions below.

1 **Who was born first?**

- ○ Mark
- ○ the dog
- ○ Jane

2 **What do you know about Jane and Mark?**

- ○ They like to run races.
- ○ They are not the same.
- ○ They are tall.

3 **What can you tell about Mark?**

- ○ He has a horse.
- ○ He likes animals.
- ○ He can't swim.

4 **Does Jane like to be outside? How do you know?**

_____

_____

_____

_____

_____

_____

_____

_____

Read the selection. Answer the questions that follow.

A New Place

Jake had to move. His mom had a new job in a new town. Jake was sad. He did not want to leave his friends or go to a new school. When it was time to move, Jake just sat on his bed. Then he sat on the rug with his trucks. His dad came to find him. They talked together for a long time. Then Jake felt much better.

Turn the page.

Answer the questions below.

1 **What happened first in the story?**

○ Jake felt better.

○ Jake sat on his bed.

○ Jake talked with his dad.

2 **Why did Jake sit in his room?**

○ He wanted to play with his trucks.

○ He had to pack his trucks in a box.

○ He did not want to move.

3 **What made Jake feel sad?**

○ He had lost his trucks.

○ He would miss his friends.

○ He wanted a new school.

4 **Dad wanted to**

○ help Jake.

○ say hi to Jake.

○ trick Jake.

5 **Why do you think Jake felt better at the end of the story?**

_____

- -

_____

_____

- -

_____

_____

- -

_____

Read the selection. Answer the questions that follow.

Changes

A moth lays its eggs on leaves. The eggs hatch. Baby caterpillars push their way out of the eggs. The caterpillars eat the leaves and grow very fast. When the caterpillars are full size, they hang from leaves. They make a pupa for their home. They change inside it. They may wait for one week or for a few years. At last moths crawl out. They dry their wings. Then they fly away.

Turn the page.

Answer the questions below.

1 **What hatches from a moth's eggs?**

- ○ caterpillars
- ○ moths
- ○ birds

2 **Why are leaves important for baby caterpillars?**

- ○ Leaves are shade.
- ○ Leaves are a hiding place.
- ○ Leaves are food.

3 **What happens after the new moths crawl out?**

- ○ They lay eggs.
- ○ They fly away.
- ○ They eat leaves.

4 **What happens to the caterpillars inside pupas?**

_____

- -

_____

_____

- -

_____

5 **Why do caterpillars grow so big and fast?**

_____

- -

_____

_____

- -

_____

Read the selection. Answer the questions that follow.

Let's Ride!

People have made many things to ride in. First they made ships to go on water. Then there were cars to go on the ground. Now planes fly in the sky. Where will people go next?

Answer the questions below.

1 **How are cars and planes the same?**

○ They both fly in the sky.

○ They both have wings.

○ They both are made by people.

2 **Which thing did people make first?**

○ ships

○ planes

○ cars

3 **What did people make last?**

○ planes

○ cars

○ ships

4 **What do you think people will make next?**

_____

- -

_____

- -

_____

- -

_____

- -

_____

- -

_____

Read the selection. Answer the questions that follow.

Play Date

Jan woke up. It was a beautiful day! She wanted to run outside and play. But she had to eat. Next she had to do some chores. Then she had to feed her fish. At last, Jan went out to play. She saw a friend down the block.

"Hi, Pam!" Jan yelled. "Do you want to play with me?"

Pam looked up. "Yes, I do!" Pam yelled back. Then Pam gave Jan a big hug.

Turn the page.

Answer the questions below.

1 **How are Pam and Jan the same?**

○ They both want to play.

○ They both feed their fish.

○ They both have chores.

2 **What did Jan do first?**

○ She ran out to play.

○ She yelled to Pam.

○ She woke up and ate.

3 **What did Jan do next?**

○ She fed her fish.

○ She did her chores.

○ She saw her friend.

4 **What did Jan do after she did some chores?**

○ She ate.

○ She fed her fish.

○ She woke up.

5 **What is the last thing that happened in the story?**

_____

- -

_____

- -

_____

- -

Read the selection. Answer the questions that follow.

The Magic Feather

One day a bird grew a beautiful magic feather that let her make one wish. She saw that farmers needed rain for their plants. She made a wish and soon rain fell for them. Then the feather gave her one more wish. She met a hippo who could not read. She wished. Soon he could read. The bird made no wishes of her own. Soon all her feathers had become magic. She was glad to make others happy.

Turn the page.

Answer the questions below.

1 **Who did the bird help first?**

○ some farmers

○ a hippo

○ a magic feather

2 **How were the farmers and the hippo the same?**

○ They both needed rain.

○ They both needed help.

○ They both grew feathers.

3 **What happened after the bird met a hippo?**

○ The bird grew one magic feather.

○ The bird met some farmers.

○ The bird helped the hippo.

4 **What happened last in the story?**

_____

- -

_____

- -

_____

5 **What was the first wish made in the story?**

_____

- -

_____

- -

_____

Read the selection. Answer the questions that follow.

Growing Plants

Some people grow plants in their homes. These are "houseplants." People enjoy smelling the flowers and seeing the leaves.

Plants need sun and water to live. Outside they need sunshine and rain. When plants live inside, people must water them.

Answer the questions below.

1 **Sunshine makes plants**

  ○ dark.

  ○ cold.

  ○ grow.

2 **What can happen if plants do not get water?**

  ○ The plants will not live.

  ○ The plants will become green.

  ○ The plants will get flowers.

3 **Why do many people have houseplants?**

  ○ They want to have food around.

  ○ They enjoy growing plants inside.

  ○ They need to have some water.

4 **Why do people have to water houseplants?**

_____

- -

_____

_____

- -

_____

- -

_____

_____

- -

_____

- -

_____

Read the selection. Answer the questions that follow.

Flowers for Sale!

A man came to the park every week. He was selling

flowers to the people there. He walked around calling,

"Flowers for sale!"

A girl said, "You can sell me roses."

"I have no roses to sell," the man said. "Would you like

some mums or a daisy?"

"Not now," the girl said. "I just want roses."

The man came back the next week. This time he had roses

for the girl.

"I do not want roses now," she said. "I just want mums."

Answer the questions below.

1 **Why did the man come to the park?**

○ to sell flowers

○ to visit his family

○ to meet his friends

2 **Why didn't the girl take a daisy?**

○ She likes flowers.

○ She wanted roses.

○ She wanted mums.

3 **Why did the man bring roses the next week?**

○ The girl asked for them.

○ He liked red flowers best.

○ The girl wanted a daisy.

4 **Why did the girl not get roses the next week?**

○ She asked for a daisy.

○ She had gotten roses before.

○ She wanted mums now.

5 **How do you think the man felt when the girl did not take the roses?**

_____

- -

_____

_____

- -

_____

_____

- -

_____

© Pearson Education 1

Read the selection. Answer the questions that follow.

Surprise!

Maria was a new girl at our school, and she had a surprise party for our class. She was afraid no one would enjoy it, but it was wonderful!

Maria's mother played the guitar. Her father made tortillas. They got a piñata. We took turns hitting it. At last Maria hit it, and it broke open. Confetti and presents fell all over the ground. We had a good time!

Maria had one more surprise. Our class will get to make a piñata!

Turn the page.

Answer the questions below.

1 **What fell out of the piñata?**

○ confetti

○ nuts

○ tortillas

2 **Why did Maria have a party for her class?**

○ It was her birthday.

○ Her family came home.

○ She was new at school.

3 **What broke the piñata?**

○ It fell down.

○ It was surprised.

○ Maria hit it.

4 **What was Maria's other surprise for the class?**

_____

_____

_____

_____

5 **Why did Maria worry about her surprise for the class?**

_____

_____

_____

_____

Fresh Reads   Unit 4 Week 1 A

© Pearson Education 1

Read the selection. Answer the questions that follow.

Two Birds with One Home

Two birds wanted to share one tree. How could they?

"I know!" Hummingbird said. "You eat bugs and live in the trunk."

Woodpecker said, "You eat nectar and make your nest on branches. We can do it!"

And they did.

Turn the page.

Answer the questions below.

1 **What is this story trying to teach?**

  ○ a way to make a nest

  ○ a way to share with others

  ○ a way to be like a bird

2 **What is the big idea in this story?**

  ○ sharing

  ○ bluebirds

  ○ eating

3 **What would be another good name for this story?**

  ○ Bugs in the Trees

  ○ Having Friends

  ○ Working Together

4 **How were the two birds able to live in the same tree together?**

_____

_____

_____

_____

_____

_____

_____

_____

Read the selection. Answer the questions that follow.

Sun and Sea

Sea was sad. She wanted friends.

One day Sun called, "Let's be friends and play together."

"But you're in the sky," said Sea. "I'm down here. How can we play?"

How could they be friends when they were so far away? They wanted to play. They had to find a way. They had to think.

Then they saw how they could play together. Sea would splash and wave to Sun. Sun would smile and shine on Sea. Now they are happy friends.

Turn the page.

Answer the questions below.

1 **When did Sun and Sea play together?**

○ in the dark

○ in the day

○ at night

2 **What is this story all about?**

○ working together to make friends

○ saying good-bye

○ splashing and talking

3 **Sea and Sun had to find a way to**

○ be sad.

○ play together.

○ go up and down.

4 **What does this story teach you about friends?**

○ Friends can help each other.

○ Friends need to stay far away.

○ Friends can be mean.

5 **How did Sun and Sea become friends?**

_____

- -

_____

_____

- -

_____

_____

- -

_____

Read the selection. Answer the questions that follow.

Greg's First Art Show

Greg hopes to be a great artist. He wants to have a show. Greg experiments with colors and shapes. He splashes bright paints on paper. He uses beautiful colors to make circles or boxes. Then he draws straight lines. Greg adds gold squiggles as a surprise. He does many new things. At last Greg makes signs for his show. People come to see his art. They like what they see. They tell Greg that he'll be a great artist some day.

Turn the page.

Answer the questions below.

1 **What is the big idea in this story?**

○ Greg paints a wall.

○ Greg makes a mess.

○ Greg has a show.

2 **Why does Greg experiment?**

○ He sells signs to people.

○ He wants to learn about painting.

○ He wants to be paid.

3 **What would be another good name for this story?**

○ A New Artist

○ Greg's School

○ How to Make Paints

4 **Why does Greg make signs for his show?**

_____

_____

_____

_____

5 **What do you think Greg will do next?**

_____

_____

_____

_____

Read the selection. Answer the questions that follow.

A Great Ride!

Once people couldn't fly. People stayed on the land or the sea. Now we have planes. Planes let people fly a long way in a short time. Some are big enough for many people to ride in. Planes are great!

Turn the page.

Answer the questions below.

1 Before planes, people could have ridden in

○ planes.

○ boats.

○ jets.

2 This story was

○ sad.

○ funny.

○ real.

3 Why do you think the author wrote this?

○ to make you happy

○ to teach you how to fly

○ to tell about planes

4 How do you think the author feels about planes? Why?

_____

_____

_____

_____

_____

_____

_____

_____

Read the selection. Answer the questions that follow.

How About a Lizard?

Are you looking for a pet? There are many wonderful pets. What would you like best? Cats and dogs are pets with soft fur. Gerbils and rabbits have soft fur too. Birds are pets with feathers in beautiful colors. Frogs and fish are pets that like the water. Would you enjoy a lizard? Every pet needs good food and a safe home. If you do get a pet, you'll need to take good care of it.

Turn the page.

Answer the questions below.

1 **What is one thing the author does not try to do?**

- ○ tell which pet is the best
- ○ tell about many kinds of pets
- ○ tell how to take care of a pet

2 **What does the author think is good about cats and dogs?**

- ○ They have soft fur.
- ○ They eat good food.
- ○ They mostly live in water.

3 **The author wrote this story to**

- ○ show you how to care for animals.
- ○ tell you about pets.
- ○ teach you about one pet.

4 **This story is**

- ○ sad.
- ○ funny.
- ○ real.

5 **How do you think the author feels about pets?**

_____

_____

_____

_____

_____

Read the selection. Answer the questions that follow.

Summer Camp

Dear Jack,

I am sending you a big "hi" from Montana! I wish you were here! This camp is so much fun. I have made many new friends. My team is called the Bandannas. We all look like cowboys. We can ride the horses. We have a campfire every night. The leader plays his guitar for us, and we sing songs.

I will mail this letter to you today, and then I will bring a present for you when I come back home! Write back soon!

Your friend,

Anna

Turn the page.

Answer the questions below.

1 **This letter is**

○ sad.

○ silly.

○ real.

2 **Why does Anna write about camp?**

○ She wants to go home.

○ She wants to tell about what she does at camp.

○ She wants to tell about horses.

3 **"Summer Camp" was written to**

○ show how to ride a horse.

○ make you cry.

○ tell about a camp.

4 **Why did Anna say, "I wish you were here!"?**

_____

- -

_____

- -

_____

5 **How do you think this letter would make Jack feel?**

_____

- -

_____

- -

_____

Read the selection. Answer the questions that follow.

Being Stubborn

"Go away!" said Dog.

But Cat wouldn't go. Cat said, "I just like walking here."

So Dog ran after Cat. Cat went up a tree. Cat looked down at Dog.

"Why did you chase me?" Cat asked.

"I just like to chase cats!" laughed Dog.

Turn the page.

Answer the questions below.

1 **What is the big idea in this story?**

○ being stubborn

○ walking

○ having pets

2 **What in this story can happen in real life?**

○ A cat can talk.

○ A dog can chase a cat.

○ A dog can laugh.

3 **What is something that can't really happen?**

○ Animals talk together.

○ A cat climbs a tree.

○ A dog runs after a cat.

4 **How can you tell this story is not real?**

_____

- -

_____

- -

_____

- -

_____

- -

_____

Read the selection. Answer the questions that follow.

Big Fish in a Small Lake

A little fish lived in a small lake. He grew up very fast. Soon he was the biggest fish in the lake. Still he kept growing bigger. At last he said, "I need a bigger home."

As fast as he could go, the fish went splashing off to the far end of the lake. He jumped up and out of the water. He flew high in the air! He went far! When he landed in the water again, he was out in the beautiful sea! The sea was so big that he seemed small again.

Turn the page.

Answer the questions below.

1 **What part of this story is not real?**

   ○ A fish talks.

   ○ A fish lives in a lake.

   ○ A fish gets bigger.

2 **Why did the fish seem smaller at the end of the story?**

   ○ He was far away.

   ○ He stopped growing.

   ○ He was in a bigger place.

3 **A real fish does not**

   ○ live in the water.

   ○ live in a lake.

   ○ fly in the air.

4 **What could really happen?**

   ○ A fish flies far away.

   ○ A fish grows very big.

   ○ A fish wants a new house.

5 **What is one way the fish in the story is like a real fish?**

_____

- -

_____

_____

- -

_____

_____

- -

_____

Read the selection. Answer the questions that follow.

Funny Festival

Dear Dad,

Will you please take me to the funny festival? It starts in three days. I would like to go there with you. It should have many surprises for us to share together. We could laugh and sing along with the caterpillar. We could hear the pig read its poem and then see it fly away. We could touch the zebra with the green spots. We could both eat some fresh pears. I know we will find a surprise or two, and we'll have great fun. Let's go!

Your son,

Jeff

Turn the page.

Answer the questions below.

1 **What could not happen in real life?**

○ A zebra could have green spots.

○ A boy could go to a festival.

○ A son could send a letter to his dad.

2 **How do you know that the funny festival is not real?**

○ People do eat fresh pears.

○ Festivals have surprises.

○ Caterpillars laugh and sing.

3 **What is the big idea in this letter?**

○ Dad and Jeff eat pears.

○ A boy wants to go to a festival.

○ A pig reads a poem.

4 **What part of Jeff's letter could be real?**

_____

- -

_____

- -

_____

5 **How do you know the pig is not real?**

_____

- -

_____

- -

_____

Read the selection. Answer the questions that follow.

Sunny Day

Max was outside playing in his yard. Max enjoyed playing by himself.

Then Carl walked over. "Can I play with you?" Carl asked.

Max said, "Yes!"

Carl was glad to play with Max. Max was happy too. Max enjoyed playing with his friends even more.

Turn the page.

Answer the questions below.

1 **What is the big idea in this story?**
- ○ playing
- ○ sunshine
- ○ school

2 **Where did this story happen?**
- ○ at the school
- ○ at Carl's house
- ○ in Max's yard

3 **What happened at the beginning of the story?**
- ○ Max played with Carl.
- ○ Max talked with Carl.
- ○ Max played by himself.

4 **From this story, what can you tell that Carl likes to do?**

_____

- -

_____

_____

- -

_____

_____

- -

_____

_____

- -

_____

Read the selection. Answer the questions that follow.

At the Park

One day some friends were playing outside.

"Fred, give other children a turn on the swing," called

Fred's mother.

Fred wanted to stay on the swing.

"Jimmy, share your ball," called Jimmy's mother.

Jimmy didn't want to share the ball.

"May, let the other children share your jump rope," called

May's mother.

May didn't want to share the jump rope.

Then Kathy came. She said, "Let's work on a fort together.

We can have fun if we all help."

The others ran over. They all said, "I want to help."

So the children all made a fort and had fun playing

together.

Turn the page.

Answer the questions below.

1 **What is the big idea in this story?**

○ It's fun to jump rope.

○ It's hard to make a fort.

○ It's fun to play together.

2 **Where does this story happen?**

○ at the park

○ at Kathy's house

○ at the school

3 **What happened at the beginning of the story?**

○ Kathy came to the park.

○ Fred was on the swing.

○ The children made a fort.

4 **What happened at the end of the story?**

○ The children jumped rope.

○ The children played together.

○ The children wouldn't share.

5 **What did Kathy do in the story?**

_____

- -

_____

- -

_____

- -

_____

Read the selection. Answer the questions that follow.

Maria's Visit

Maria wanted to visit the animals at the shelter. She made biscuits for the dogs and cookies for the cats. Then Maria took the bus to the shelter. When Maria got there she saw many cats playing in a room. Maria went inside and fed them the cookies. Then she went outside to see the dogs. They ran around the yard and barked at everything. She enjoyed feeding them the biscuits. At last it was time for Maria to go home. She told the animals she would come back soon.

Turn the page.

Answer the questions below.

1 **What happened at the beginning of this story?**

○ Maria made treats for the animals.

○ The cats ate Maria's cookies.

○ Maria gave biscuits to the dogs.

2 **How did Maria feel about feeding the animals?**

○ worried

○ happy

○ afraid

3 **What is the big idea in this story?**

○ Maria likes to help animals.

○ Maria likes to bake cookies.

○ Maria likes to ride the bus.

4 **Where did Maria see the dogs playing?**

_____

- -

_____

- -

_____

5 **What happened at the end of this story?**

_____

- -

_____

- -

_____

Read the selection. Answer the questions that follow.

Dance Class

Ling didn't like dance class. Kids made fun of her.

Every week she asked, "Dad, must I go?"

Dad was sad. He wanted Ling to enjoy it.

Dad said, "If you just do your best, they'll be nice."

He was right! Ling became happy again.

Turn the page.

Answer the questions below.

1 **How did Ling feel at the beginning of the story?**

- ○ happy
- ○ afraid
- ○ sad

2 **Why didn't Ling like her dance class?**

- ○ Other kids picked on her.
- ○ The class was too hard.
- ○ Dad made her go to class.

3 **What made Ling's father sad?**

- ○ He did not want Ling to dance.
- ○ He did not like to drive Ling to class.
- ○ Ling did not like the dance class.

4 **What made Ling happy at the end of the story?**

_____

_____

_____

_____

_____

_____

_____

_____

_____

_____

Read the selection. Answer the questions that follow.

Rose's Plane Trip

Rose and Mother will take a plane trip to visit Grandmother. Grandmother's home is far away. Rose is a little afraid. She has never gotten on a plane before. It will be very new to her!

Rose and Mother wait in long lines. Nice people smile at them. Rose smiles back. Rose starts to feel better. Now it's their turn! They get on the plane. Rose likes the little tray at her seat. She likes the snacks too. Rose looks out the window to see the ground below. Flying is fun!

Turn the page.

Answer the questions below.

1 **How was Rose feeling at the beginning of the story?**

- ○ very happy
- ○ a little afraid
- ○ a bit sad

2 **Why do Rose and Mother go on the plane trip?**

- ○ to visit Grandmother far away
- ○ to wait in line
- ○ to eat snacks

3 **Rose is a little afraid to fly because**

- ○ it will be her first time on a plane.
- ○ Mother is there with her.
- ○ the people are so nice.

4 **What makes Rose feel better?**

- ○ Rose talks to Grandmother.
- ○ Rose talks to Mother.
- ○ People smile at Rose.

5 **What makes Rose think it is fun to fly?**

_____

_____

_____

_____

Read the selection. Answer the questions that follow.

Be Careful!

Jean got dressed for school in a hurry. She forgot she had to tie the laces on her new shoes very tightly. Jean almost forgot she needed to take treats today too. Mom gave Jean a bag of cookies. Jean carried it as she left the house.

Because her shoelaces were not tight enough, Jean's shoe came loose. Jean tripped on the back steps and dropped the bag. The cookies broke.

"Be careful," said Mom. She gave Jean more cookies. Jean took the new bag and left. But first she tied her shoelaces tightly!

Turn the page.

Answer the questions below.

1 **Why did Jean's shoe come loose?**

○ The laces were not tied tightly.

○ Jean's socks were not dry.

○ Jean walked down the steps.

2 **What made Jean trip?**

○ The steps were wet.

○ She was in a hurry.

○ Her shoe was loose.

3 **Where did Jean trip?**

○ at the school

○ on the back steps

○ at the park

4 **Why did the cookies break?**

_____

- -

_____

- -

_____

5 **Why did Jean tie her shoelaces tightly before she left the house again?**

_____

- -

_____

_____

- -

_____

Read the selection. Answer the questions that follow.

Lucy and the Snake

Every day Lucy went to the well for water. She would carry it to the house. She always walked along the path. One day she saw a snake on the path. Lucy was brave. She stopped and was still. She waited. The snake passed. When it was gone, Lucy walked on home.

Turn the page.

Answer the questions below.

1 **What was Lucy like?**

- ○ brave
- ○ silly
- ○ funny

2 **Where did Lucy stand and wait for the snake?**

- ○ in her house
- ○ on the path
- ○ in the water

3 **What happened at the end of the story?**

- ○ Lucy went back home.
- ○ Lucy saw a snake.
- ○ Lucy walked to the well.

4 **What is the big idea in this story?**

_____

_____

_____

_____

_____

_____

_____

_____

_____

Read the selection. Answer the questions that follow.

Henry's Train Set

Henry had a train set with train cars in many colors. It had tracks for the cars to move on. Henry set up the train in his room. He put the tracks down in the shape of an eight. Henry watched the train run around the tracks. It went under the hills and over the water. What fun!

Henry had a little sister, Mary. She wanted to play with it too.

"You are too little!" said Henry. "I would have to teach you how to play with it."

"I am not," said Mary. "You just don't want to share it."

Henry thought it over and said, "It is your turn to teach me! You're right. I'm sorry. Let's play together!"

Turn the page.

Answer the questions below.

1 **What happens at the beginning of the story?**

○ Henry sets up his train set in his room.

○ Mary wants to play with the train.

○ Henry asks Mary to play with him.

2 **How do you think Mary feels at the end?**

○ too little to play with trains

○ happy that she spoke up

○ afraid of Henry

3 **Where does this story take place?**

○ in the yard

○ at the school

○ in Henry's room

4 **What happens at the end of the story?**

○ Henry tells Mary to go away.

○ Henry asks Mary to play.

○ Henry sets up the train tracks.

5 **What is the big idea of this story?**

_____

_____

_____

_____

_____

Read the selection. Answer the questions that follow.

Gigantic Fun

There once was a giant who wanted to play with the trolls. But they never asked him to play.

"You are too big," they told him. "We worry that you might step on us!"

"I'll watch out. I won't hurt you!" he said. "And I'm not too big. I'm just right. Let me show you!"

The giant took the trolls to his favorite place in the forest. He gave them a ride on the top of his head. They had never been so high! They could see far! Together, they built a play house high up in the leaves. What a great spot to have fun!

Turn the page.

Answer the questions below.

1 At the beginning of the story, the trolls think the giant is

○ not fair.

○ too big.

○ always mad.

2 How does the giant feel at the end of the story?

○ happy

○ afraid

○ sad

3 What is the big idea in this story?

○ playing on the ground

○ making new friends

○ going up in the trees

4 Where do the giant and the trolls build their play house?

_____

_____

_____

5 How do the trolls feel about the giant at the end of the story?

_____

_____

_____

Read the selection. Answer the questions that follow.

A Walk in the Park

Peg wanted to go for a walk in the park. She would take along her dog, Max. They both went down the steps. They walked outside. It was raining!

They went back inside and back up the steps. Peg put on her raincoat. Now they could go back out on their walk!

Turn the page.

Answer the questions below.

1 **What would be the best name for this story?**

  ◯ A Walk on a Sunny Day

  ◯ Cold Winters in the City

  ◯ Can We Go Walking Yet?

2 **What was the first thing that Peg did?**

  ◯ She went outside.

  ◯ She went down the steps.

  ◯ She saw it was raining.

3 **What happened as soon as Peg saw that it was raining?**

  ◯ Peg and Max went back up the steps.

  ◯ Peg and Max went down the steps.

  ◯ Peg and Max went on their walk.

4 **What happened last in the story?**

_____

- -

_____

- -

_____

- -

_____

- -

_____

- -

_____

Read the selection. Answer the questions that follow.

A Dinner for Mother

Mark and Dad are going to make a chicken dinner for Mother. She will be getting home from a long trip tonight. They want her to feel loved when she gets home. They are going to give her a very nice meal.

First Mark washes his hands. Then Dad washes his hands. Next they clean the chicken. After that they put salt and pepper on the chicken. Next they need to bake the chicken for two hours. It smells so good!

While the chicken bakes, Dad makes rice. Mark makes peas. This will be a good dinner! And here is Mother walking in the door!

Turn the page.

Answer the questions below.

1 **What is this story all about?**

- ○ seeing Mark's mother
- ○ getting dinner
- ○ going on a trip

2 **What does Mark do first?**

- ○ washes his hands
- ○ bakes a chicken
- ○ makes the peas

3 **What does Mark do next?**

- ○ washes his hands
- ○ bakes the chicken
- ○ cleans the chicken

4 **What is the last thing that happens in the story?**

- ○ Mark makes peas.
- ○ Mother comes home.
- ○ Dad makes rice.

5 **What two things happen just after Mark and Dad clean the chicken?**

_____

- -

_____

- -

_____

Read the selection. Answer the questions that follow.

A Treasure Hunt

Sue was in a contest with friends. Everyone got to go on a treasure hunt. Each kid had a list of things to find. The first one to bring back all those things would win.

Sue wanted to win. She would have to get everything on her list. First, she knocked on her neighbor's door. She borrowed a feather hat. Next, she found a maple tree. She pulled a leaf from a branch. Then, Sue dug a hole and pulled out a worm. Last, she drew a heart on paper. Sue made a Valentine's Day card.

She was the winner of the treasure hunt!

Turn the page.

Answer the questions below.

1 The first thing that Sue got was

   ○ a card.

   ○ a bird cage.

   ○ a hat.

2 After Sue dug a hole, she

   ○ pulled out a worm.

   ○ planted a seed.

   ○ filled it with water.

3 What is this story all about?

   ○ looking for birds

   ○ trying to win a contest

   ○ seeing the neighborhood

4 What did Sue do just after she got the hat?

_____

_____

_____

_____

5 How did Sue get the last thing on her list?

_____

_____

_____

_____

Read the selection. Answer the questions that follow.

Making Boats Go

People made boats to ride on water. First they had to row

with oars to make them go. It was hard work to paddle! Then

they used sails to catch the wind. Wind could push "sailboats"

across the water. Later, people used steam to make boats go.

The "steamboats" made it easy!

Turn the page.

Answer the questions below.

1 **What is this story all about?**

○ making boats move

○ being on a ship

○ how to drive a boat

2 **How were steamboats not like the first boats?**

○ The first boats used steam to go.

○ The steamboats were hard to move.

○ The steamboats were easy to ride on water.

3 **How are sailboats and steamboats the same?**

○ They are both easy to move.

○ They both use steam to go.

○ They are both hard work!

4 **What is another way that sailboats and steamboats are alike?**

_____

_____

_____

_____

_____

_____

_____

_____

_____

Read the selection. Answer the questions that follow.

Two Friends

Hummingbird was feeling sad. He thought he would feel better spending time with his pal, Elephant.

"Would you come out with me?" Hummingbird asked him.

"I'd like to go walking in the forest," Elephant told him.

It was fun seeing the two go side by side! Elephant walked on the path. Hummingbird flew along with him. Elephant was so big, and his skin was all wrinkled and dark. Hummingbird was so very small, and he had feathers in bright, beautiful colors.

They talked as they went. They liked to be together in the forest. At the end of the day, Hummingbird was happy again.

Turn the page.

Answer the questions below.

1 **What happened in the middle of this story?**

- ○ Hummingbird was feeling sad.
- ○ Hummingbird went out with Elephant.
- ○ Hummingbird was happy again.

2 **How are Hummingbird and Elephant the same?**

- ○ They both are about the same size.
- ○ They both have bright feathers.
- ○ They both like being in the forest.

3 **How is Hummingbird not the same as Elephant?**

- ○ Hummingbird can fly, and Elephant cannot.
- ○ Hummingbird is an animal, and Elephant is not.
- ○ Elephant has wings, and Hummingbird does not.

4 **In this story Hummingbird and Elephant both**

- ○ are big.
- ○ can talk.
- ○ can fly.

5 **What is another way that Hummingbird and Elephant are not alike?**

_____

_____

_____

_____

_____

_____

Read the selection. Answer the questions that follow.

Squirrels

Gail is a gray squirrel. Rod is a red squirrel. They both live in trees. Gail and her gray squirrel family sleep in nests. Because Rod is a red squirrel, he sleeps alone.

Gray squirrels like to eat nuts, seeds, and bugs. They dig holes in which to store their food. Then they have things to eat in winter. Red squirrels eat pine cones and nuts. They hide them in places like stone walls so they have food in winter too.

When there is danger, squirrels warn each other. Gray squirrels wave their bushy tails. Red squirrels stamp their feet. This lets the other squirrels know that there is danger.

Turn the page.

Answer the questions below.

1 This story is all about
○ house pets.
○ bird watching.
○ forest animals.

2 How are gray squirrels and red squirrels the same?
○ Both sleep alone.
○ Both store winter food.
○ Both are the same color.

3 What is one way that gray squirrels are not like red squirrels?
○ They eat bugs.
○ They warn of danger.
○ They live in trees.

4 What do red squirrels and gray squirrels eat that is the same?

_____

- -

_____

- -

_____

5 How are the two kinds of squirrels not the same?

_____

- -

_____

- -

_____

Read the selection. Answer the questions that follow.

Pack Your Trunk!

Elephants have long trunks. Trunks are more than just noses! Elephants use their trunks to do many things. Elephants fill them with water and use them like hoses! They drink by spraying water into their mouths. They can spray water over their backs and get wet instead. Elephants use them to smell and touch. They can even scratch an itch!

Turn the page.

Answer the questions below.

1 **Which sentence best tells what this story is all about?**

- ○ Elephants drink by spraying water into their mouths.
- ○ Elephants can even scratch an itch!
- ○ Elephants use their trunks to do many things.

2 **What is this story all about?**

- ○ elephants using their trunks
- ○ elephant families
- ○ elephants drinking water

3 **What is the another good name for this story?**

- ○ Water Hoses
- ○ An Elephant's Tool Kit
- ○ Wet Animals

4 **How is an elephant's trunk not the same as a person's nose?**

_____

_____

_____

_____

_____

_____

_____

_____

_____

Read the selection. Answer the questions that follow.

The Common Cold

Getting sick with a cold is not any fun. Your nose is all stuffed up. Your head hurts. You sneeze too. It is hard to feel good when you have a cold.

A cold is called "the common cold" because so many people get one. People usually get them in the winter. Sometimes a cold hits you in the summer! The sun is shining. The birds are singing. And you are sick in bed. It isn't fair! Drink lots of water. Get your rest. You'll feel better soon!

There are things that you can do to help keep colds away. The biggest thing is washing your hands. When your hands are clean, the common cold may be much less common.

Turn the page.

Answer the questions below.

1 **This story is mostly about how to handle**

- ○ winter.
- ○ colds.
- ○ washing.

2 **What is this story all about?**

- ○ dealing with the common cold
- ○ being inside in the summer
- ○ playing outside in the sun

3 **What would be another good name for this story?**

- ○ Don't Get Sick!
- ○ How the Birds Sing
- ○ Cleaning Up

4 **Which sentence best tells what this story is all about?**

- ○ The sun shines in the summer.
- ○ It gets cold in the winter.
- ○ People must deal with colds.

5 **Why is it so hard to have a cold in the summer?**

_____

_____

_____

_____

Read the selection. Answer the questions that follow.

Skunks on Defense

Skunks have a spray that smells very bad. It is called musk. They spray musk to chase away all their enemies. They use it when they are afraid. They only use it after they give warnings.

Before spraying, a skunk growls and bangs its feet. If the enemy comes closer, the skunk raises its tail. The tail's white tip still hangs down. One step closer and that tip goes up. That is bad news! The skunk fires two jets of spray. It stinks! The enemy goes running away from that skunk!

Only the Great Horned Owl is not afraid of skunks. These owls can swoop down and catch them before they can spray. They found the way to defeat skunks.

Turn the page.

Answer the questions below.

1 **What is this story all about?**

- ○ a dance to scare owls
- ○ a white tail to catch mice
- ○ a spray to keep enemies away

2 **This story is mostly about how skunks**

- ○ make use of musk.
- ○ go after owls.
- ○ bang their feet.

3 **Which sentence best tells what this story is all about?**

- ○ Skunks' spray does not block owls.
- ○ A skunk can usually stop its enemies.
- ○ The tail of a skunk has a white tip.

4 **What would be another good name for this story?**

_____

- -

_____

- -

_____

5 **How are the owls not the same as other enemies of the skunk?**

_____

- -

_____

- -

_____

Read the selection. Answer the questions that follow.

The Boy and the Frog

A boy was walking in the woods. He heard a voice.

"Hello, Boy!" the voice said.

"Who is calling me?" the boy asked.

"It is I. Frog. Come here."

The boy walked on. But Frog hopped along after him.

"I want to grant you a wish," said Frog.

"Then I wish you would just leave me alone!" said the boy.

Turn the page.

Answer the questions below.

1 **Why did Frog say "Come here" to the boy?**

○ Frog had heard a voice in the woods.

○ Frog wanted to hop with the boy.

○ Frog wanted the boy to stop and talk.

2 **Why did the boy walk away from Frog?**

○ He wanted to be left alone.

○ He needed a new friend.

○ He wanted to talk with Frog.

3 **Why did Frog keep following the boy?**

○ Frog wanted to go home with him.

○ Frog wanted to go on a walk with him.

○ Frog wanted to give him a wish.

4 **What is this story all about?**

_____

_____

_____

_____

_____

_____

_____

_____

Read the selection. Answer the questions that follow.

Snow Surprise

Jen woke up one day and saw that lots of snow had fallen. She just sat in bed and looked out her window at it all.

Then she called out, "School must be closed today!" No one called back to her. Jen got up and dressed.

"Mom? Dad? Is school closed today?" asked Jen. There was still no reply. Then Jen looked outside the back door. She saw Mom and Dad playing in the snow. They were making a snowman! Why weren't they getting ready to go to work?

"Hey!" Jen called. "What are you doing?"

Mom just laughed and rolled a snowball toward Jen. Jen put on her coat and mittens. Hurray! She would help them with that snowman!

Turn the page.

Answer the questions below.

1 **What is this story all about?**

○ surprises

○ cold

○ a snowman

2 **What makes you think school was closed that day?**

○ Dad told Jen that school was closed.

○ Jen looked out her window at the snow.

○ Mom and Dad could stay home from work.

3 **Why weren't Mom and Dad getting ready for work?**

○ They did not have jobs to go to.

○ The snow had shut down everything.

○ They had already gone to work.

4 **How did Jen feel when she saw Mom and Dad in the snow?**

○ scared

○ sad

○ surprised

5 **What do you think Jen is going to do next?**

_____

_____

_____

_____

_____

_____

Read the selection. Answer the questions that follow.

Mother's Day

Dear Dad,

I want you to know how things are going while you are on your trip.

I wanted to surprise Mom on Mother's Day. I wanted to do nice things for her to show her how much I love her. I got up early and ran the vacuum. It was so heavy that it pulled down the curtains in the living room. Then I made Mom's favorite food. I never knew that eggs could stick to walls! Mom was surprised when she saw that I had mowed the whole lawn, along with most of her flowers.

Mom said that I gave her more surprises than she really needed. Mom said she still loves me too.

Come home soon.

> Love,
>
> Tim

Turn the page.

Answer the questions below.

1 **Where does this story take place?**

- ○ at school
- ○ at home
- ○ at camp

2 **What did Tim want to do?**

- ○ make a big mess at home
- ○ make more work for Mom
- ○ help Mom around the house

3 **Tim wrote this letter because his father**

- ○ was not home for Mother's Day.
- ○ did not like to get phone calls.
- ○ taught him how to cook eggs.

4 **What happened when Tim cooked Mom breakfast?**

_____

_____

_____

_____

5 **How do you think Tim felt after he tried to help Mom around the house?**

_____

_____

_____

_____

Read the selection. Answer the questions that follow.

The New Baby

Mom and Dad think Yolanda's baby brother is very cute. Yolanda isn't sure. She thinks he may be a little bit cute. But he seems to cry so much. When he is sleeping, no one can shout or sing or talk in the house. Yolanda loves him very much. But some days she wants to be an only child again!

Turn the page.

Answer the questions below.

1 **How does Yolanda feel about the baby?**

○ jealous

○ sweet

○ brave

2 **What is the big idea in this story?**

○ Babies are always fun to have around.

○ Yolanda is going to be a good baby-sitter.

○ Being a big sister can be hard at first.

3 **What did you learn about people from this story?**

○ Family changes are sometimes hard to handle.

○ Sharing toys with others is always easy.

○ Friendship is a very good thing.

4 **What makes you think that Yolanda is getting used to her new brother?**

_____

- -

_____

_____

- -

_____

_____

- -

_____

_____

- -

_____

Read the selection. Answer the questions that follow.

Enough for All

When the animals came to the water hole to get a drink, the water was all gone.

Zebra said, "What will we do?"

Elephant said, "We can dig down. We'll find water when we've made the hole deeper."

So they started to dig. They became hot and tired. But they found enough water for everyone.

"We've worked hard," they said. "We should be proud. Let's all have some cool water."

Zebra said, "Rabbit didn't help us dig. He shouldn't get any!"

"That's silly!" the other animals told Zebra. "Be kind! If Rabbit gets no water, he might not live. There is enough for us all."

Zebra thought again. "You are right. It is best to share it with every animal."

Turn the page.

Answer the questions below.

1 **Where does this story take place?**

○ in the park

○ at the water hole

○ by Rabbit's house

2 **What is the big idea in this story?**

○ learning to share

○ digging a hole

○ having some food

3 **What did you learn about friendship from this story?**

○ It is not right to share.

○ Be kind to others.

○ Listen to the elephants.

4 **What would be another good name for this story?**

○ Elephant Changes His Mind

○ Sharing with Others

○ Rabbit Digs a Hole

5 **What happened when Zebra thought again?**

_____

_____

_____

_____

Read the selection. Answer the questions that follow.

The Amazing Invention

Tom wanted to be a great inventor. He entered a contest for people who had ideas for making new things. Tom wanted to invent something that would help a child learn to play the piano.

Tom worked on his invention. He wanted to make a new kind of piano keyboard with lights over each key. When a light blinked, the child would play that piano key. For every song, Tom had to make the lights go on and off just right. It was hard work.

At first, Tom could not get his invention to work right. He kept trying. He learned from his mistakes. At last he found out how to make it work. He built another keyboard.

Tom won first prize!

Turn the page.

Answer the questions below.

1 **What is the big idea in this story?**

- ○ Do not tell lies.
- ○ Keep on trying.
- ○ Remember old friends.

2 **What did you learn about Tom from this story?**

- ○ He likes to play guitar.
- ○ He doesn't like hard work.
- ○ He doesn't give up.

3 **When Tom made a mistake, he**

- ○ tried to use it to do better.
- ○ stopped inventing anything.
- ○ threw away his invention.

4 **What happened to Tom at the end of the story?**

_____

_____

_____

_____

5 **What do you think Tom would have done if he hadn't won this contest?**

_____

_____

_____

_____